VENTURE TO THE INTERIOR

By the same Author

IN A PROVINCE